THE GREAT BIBLE Discovery

HOSEA AND ISAIAH

THE BIBLE IS A BEST-SELLER. IT IS ALSO ONE OF THE MASTER-WORKS OF WORLD LITERATURE - SO IMPORTANT THAT UNIVERSITIES TODAY TEACH 'NON-RELIGIOUS' BIBLE COURSES TO HELP STUDENTS WHO CHOOSE TO STUDY WESTERN LITERATURE.

THE BIBLE POSSESSES AN AMAZING POWER TO FASCINATE YOUNG AND OLD ALIKE.

ONE REASON FOR THIS UNIVERSAL APPEAL IS THAT IT DEALS WITH BASIC HUMAN LONGINGS, EMOTIONS, RELATIONSHIPS. 'ALL THE WORLD IS HERE.' ANOTHER REASON IS THAT SO MUCH OF THE BIBLE CONSISTS OF STORIES. THEY ARE FULL OF MEANING BUT EASY TO REMEMBER.

HERE ARE THOSE STORIES, PRESENTED SIMPLY AND WITH A MINIMUM OF EXPLANATION. WE HAVE LEFT THE TEXT TO SPEAK FOR ITSELF. GIFTED ARTISTS USE THE ACTION-STRIP TECHNIQUE TO BRING THE BIBLE'S DEEP MESSAGE TO READERS OF ALL AGES. THEIR DRAWINGS ARE BASED ON INFORMATION FROM ARCHAEOLOGICAL DISCOVERIES COVERING FIFTEEN CENTURIES.

AN ANCIENT BOOK - PRESENTED FOR THE PEOPLE OF THE SECOND MILLENNIUM. A RELIGIOUS BOOK - PRESENTED FREE FROM THE INTERPRETATION OF ANY PARTICULAR CHURCH. A UNIVERSAL BOOK - PRESENTED IN A FORM THAT ALL MAY ENJOY.

M publishing
CARLISLE, UK

12

C000136829

These Hebrew prophets are something really amazing. The two kingdoms where they lived so many centuries ago were tiny, compared with Egypt, Assyria or Babylonia. Yet their words are still read all over the world today.

The prophets were so unlike each other in so many ways - background, personality, way of speaking and writing. The books that bear their names differ in so many respects. And yet if we listen to them carefully we realise that they all shared a similar outlook. Their messages harmonize in a remarkable way.

Hosea is often called the prophet of loyal love - and rightly so. He knew that true love means commitment. This was true of God's covenant love for his people as well as in Hosea's own experience. Yet he was also sure that Israel would suffer for her sins.

Isaiah was just as fierce as Amos had been in denouncing people who put their trust in religious observance. Just as Amos had faced the high priest at Bethel, so Isaiah confronted kings and noblemen. But Isaiah took a far more active part in politics than Amos or Hosea. He promised that after Judah had been punished for her sins, the few faithful people who remained would be ruled by another 'son of David' who would establish peace and justice.

Times were hard when the prophets delivered their messages. Hosea saw society falling to pieces around him, while one king followed another on the throne and the threat from Assyria grew greater year by year. Isaiah was surrounded by politicians who would far rather trust in their diplomatic skills than in the Lord. His mission led him to behave in some very strange ways and also to give some bizarre names to his children - in much the same way as Hosea had done. Did the prophets find this sort of thing hard, one wonders? Come to that, did their children?

Today our circumstances are very different from theirs. In some ways at least.

But the prophets of Israel and Judah still have the power to challenge us about the way we look at life and also the way we relate to God.

HOSEA
ISAIAH 1-39
2 KINGS 14-20
2 CHRONICLES 26-32

HOSEA AND ISAIAH

First published as *Découvrir la Bible* 1983

First edition © Larousse S.A. 1984
24-volume series adaptation by Mike Jacklin © Knowledge Unlimited 1994
This edition © OM Publishing 1995

01 00 99 98 97 96 95   7 6 5 4 3 2 1

OM Publishing is an imprint of Send the Light Ltd.,
P.O. Box 300, Carlisle, Cumbria CA3 0QS, U.K.

Introductions: Peter Cousins

British Library Cataloguing in Publication Data
A catalogue record for this book is available from the British Library
ISBN 1-85078-216-4

Printed in Singapore by Tien Wah Press (Pte) Ltd.

HOSEA SINGS OF GOD'S TENDER LOVE

SCENARIO: Etienne DAHLER
DRAWING: Raymond POÏVET

IN THE COUNTRYSIDE CLOSE TO SAMARIA HOSEA TALKS TO A FRIEND...

COME WITH ME TO THE LEVITES TONIGHT.

BUT, HOSEA, THAT'S TOO DANGEROUS. THEY'VE BEEN THROWN OUT OF THE ROYAL PLACES OF WORSHIP!

BUT THEY'RE THE ONES WHO KNOW HOW TO PRESERVE THE KNOWLEDGE OF GOD — AND THERE'S LITTLE ENOUGH OF THAT IN ISRAEL TODAY.

THAT SAME NIGHT, WITH THE LEVITES...

MOSES SAID: LISTEN ISRAEL, THE LORD YOUR GOD IS ONE ... BUT THE ISRAELITES WON'T ACCEPT THAT; THEY PROSTITUTE THEMSELVES BY WORSHIPPING IDOLS!

THAT IS WHY GOD'S JUDGEMENT IS COMING CLOSER. IT IS OUR DUTY TO TELL THE PEOPLE!

HOSEA, SHOW US THE WAY, BECAUSE YOU'VE BEEN CALLED BY GOD!

LET'S GET READY TO DO THE WORK GOD WILL GIVE US.

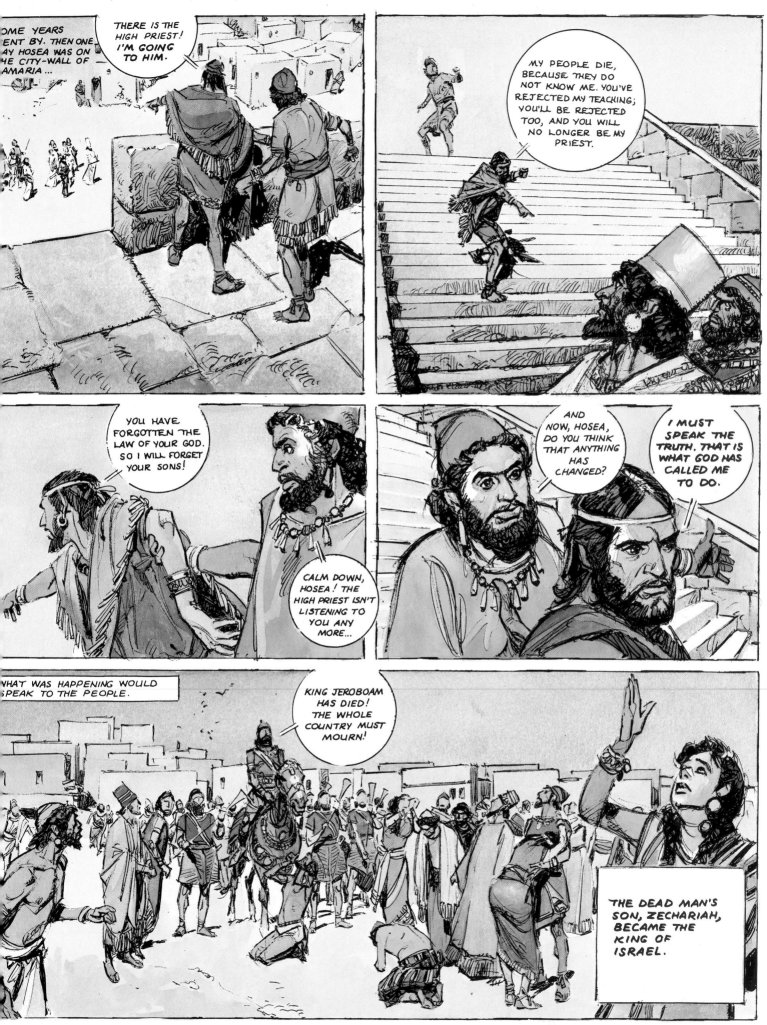

5

A FEW WEEKS LATER SHALLUM, WHO HAD ASSASSINATED THE KING, WAS ALSO MURDERED. MENAHEM BECAME KING. THERE WAS CHAOS IN THE NORTHERN KINGDOM. IN AN ALLEY IN SAMARIA, HOSEA...

SONS OF ISRAEL, HEAR THE WORD OF THE LORD...

THERE IS NOTHING BUT LYING, STEALING, MURDER, AND ADULTERY! THERE IS VIOLENCE, AND BLOOD RUNS IN OUR STREETS!

NOW THE EARTH IS DRYING UP; EVERYONE WHO LIVES ON IT IS IN DESPAIR... THE ANIMALS IN THE FIELDS, THE BIRDS IN THE SKY AND EVEN THE FISH IN THE SEA ARE GOING TO DIE!

THE GUARDS STOPPED HOSEA FROM SPEAKING...

CALM DOWN, HOSEA! GO HOME!

HE WOULD DO BETTER BY LOOKING AFTER HIS WIFE!

9

ASSYRIA BECAME POWERFUL AGAIN. ITS NEW RULER, TIGLATH-PILESER III, CARRIED ON THE POLICIES OF CONQUEST THE KINGS BEFORE HIM HAD FOLLOWED.

FORWARD MARCH! TO VICTORY!

HE INVADED ARAM AND ISRAEL, AND BROUGHT THOSE REGIONS UNDER HIS CONTROL.

ASSYRIA

NINEVEH

DAMASCUS

SAMARIA

JERUSALEM

ONCE HE HAD THE MONEY, THE KING OF ASSYRIA WENT BACK TO HIS COUNTRY, BUT HOSEA WASN'T HAPPY.

IN SAMARIA MENAHEM, KING OF ISRAEL, ALSO HAD TO PAY TRIBUTE.

GIVE THEM TO ME... AND BE FAITHFUL TO ME!

YOUR MAJESTY, HERE ARE THE 1000 TALENTS, BUT I'M COUNTING ON YOU TO KEEP ME IN POWER.

THE ISRAELITES DO NOT REALIZE IT WAS I WHO GAVE THEM CORN, WINE AND OIL... AND THE SILVER AND GOLD WHICH THEY HAVE MADE INTO A BAAL!

ALAS! WE ARE RUINED!

YES, SAYS THE LORD, I WILL PUNISH ISRAEL FOR BURNING INCENSE TO THE BAALS. BUT I'M GOING TO WOO HER AGAIN; I'LL TAKE HER INTO THE DESERT, AND SPEAK TO HER HEART.

GOMER WAS STILL BEING UNFAITHFUL TO HOSEA. SHE FELL PREGNANT AGAIN AND GAVE BIRTH TO A BOY...

WHAT ARE YOU GOING TO CALL HIM?

HOSEA HAS TOLD ME TO CALL HIM LO-'AMMI.*

*Not my people.

WHAT RIGHT HAS HE TO DO THAT? IT HAS BEEN A LONG TIME SINCE YOU LIVED AS HIS WIFE.

BUT DON'T FORGET: HE HAS NEVER DISOWNED ME.

ONE DAY HOSEA...

THE TIME HAS COME. I'M GOING TO BRING GOMER BACK.

HOSEA, HAVE YOU THOUGHT ABOUT IT CAREFULLY?

I CAN'T PUT IT OFF. THE LORD SAID TO ME: LOVE HER AS I LOVE THE PEOPLE OF ISRAEL, EVEN THOUGH THEY SERVE OTHER GODS.

WHAT A STORY! I'M CRAZY WITH JOY.

THE LORD TEACHES US TO LOVE WITHOUT LIMIT.

11

GOMER, THE PEOPLE ARE MORE AND MORE MISERABLE, AND OUR RULERS THINK ONLY OF FEASTING!

DON'T BE DISCOURAGED, HOSEA... THE LORD IS COUNTING ON YOU.

WHAT MUST I DO? THE KING'S PROPHETS ARE A GANG; THE PRIESTS ARE BRIGANDS; ARMED MOBS DESTROY THE COUNTRY...

ONE GROUP, LED BY A MAN CALLED PEKAH, ASSASSINATED KING PEKAHIAH, AND TOOK POWER.

NOW WE'RE IN CONTROL!

PEKAH, I THINK WE MUST FIRST GET FREE OF THE ASSYRIANS.

BY OURSELVES THAT IS IMPOSSIBLE! WE MUST MAKE AN ALLIANCE!

THEY GOT INTO TOUCH WITH DAMASCUS AND GAZA.

WE ALSO NEED THE KINGDOM OF JUDAH TO HELP US...

I'M AFRAID THAT WON'T BE EASY...

WE'RE GOING TO BE BESIEGED, YOUR MAJESTY. WE CAN'T HOLD OUT FOR VERY LONG!

I HAVE AN IDEA TO UP-SET THEIR PLAN...

IN JERUSALEM KING AHAZ INSPECTED THE CITY'S DEFENCES.

SEND MESSENGERS IMMEDIATELY TO WARN TIGLATH-PILESER, KING OF ASSYRIA!

THEY TOOK THE SILVER AND GOLD FROM THE TEMPLE AND THE ROYAL TREASURY TO SEND TO THE ASSYRIAN KING.

AHAZ, DON'T BE AFRAID! THIS IS WHAT THE LORD SAYS: JUDAH WON'T BE DESTROYED.

IN THE ROYAL PALACE IN JERUSALEM ISAIAH, A YOUNG PROPHET, SPOKE TO KING AHAZ... IN SPITE OF HIS ENCOURAGING WORDS, THE MESSENGERS LEFT FOR ASSYRIA.

THE WHOLE REGION IS UNDER CONTROL. THE CITY IS TIGHTLY CLOSED.

AND NOW WE WAIT! BEFORE LONG THEY'LL BE GETTING HUNGRY...

THE SIEGE OF JERUSALEM BEGAN... PEKAH OF SAMARIA AND THE KING OF ARAM WERE CAMPED IN FRONT OF THE CITY WALLS.

SOW THE WIND, AND YOU'LL REAP THE WHIRLWIND!

IN HIS DESPAIR HOSEA CRIED OUT...

WHEN THEY ARRIVED IN NINEVEH, AHAZ'S MESSENGERS GAVE THE MESSAGE TO KING TIGLATH-PILESER.

YOUR KING NEEDN'T WORRY! FIRST THING TOMORROW I'LL MARCH AGAINST ARAM AND ISRAEL...

WARNED OF THE ASSYRIAN ATTACK, THE ALLIES QUICKLY LIFTED THE **SIEGE OF JERUSALEM.**

WE'LL HAVE TO BE QUICK, IF WE WANT TO REACH SAMARIA BEFORE THE ASSYRIANS!

THIS IS AHAZ'S DOING!

ON THE WAY PEKAH AND HIS TROOPS SACKED PART OF THE LAND OF JUDAH. THEN THEY SHUT THEMSELVES INSIDE THE CITADEL OF SAMARIA.

THE FAILURE OF THE ALLIANCE LED TO THE DEATH OF KING PEKAH.

EVERYTHING IS READY, **HOSHEA BEN-ELAH!**

THAT IS FINE! TOMORROW, THEN!

17

THE LEADING PEOPLE OF SAMARIA PAID HOMAGE TO THEIR NEW KING... WHILE HOSEA PROPHESIED...

KING HOSHEA BEN-ELAH, I ACKNOWLEDGE YOU AS GOD'S CHOSEN ONE.

THEY SPEAK EMPTY WORDS; THEY MAKE PROMISES WHICH MEAN NOTHING; THEY BREAK CONTRACTS... WHILE THE PUNISHMENT GROWS LIKE POISONOUS WEEDS IN THE FURROWS OF THE FIELDS!

AND HERE WE ARE, UNDER ASSYRIA AGAIN!

THERE WAS NO OTHER WAY. KING HOSHEA BEN-ELAH WAS RIGHT.

BUT THE PROPHET HOSEA WAS ALSO RIGHT WHEN HE SAID THAT THE GREAT KING OF NINEVEH WOULDN'T BE ABLE TO HEAL OUR WOUNDS.

THE NORTHERN KINGDOM GRADUALLY RECOVERED FROM THE WAR ...

THE INVADERS ALSO SACKED THE HOLY PLACE AT BETHEL.

THEY'RE TAKING EVERYTHING AWAY FROM US!

18

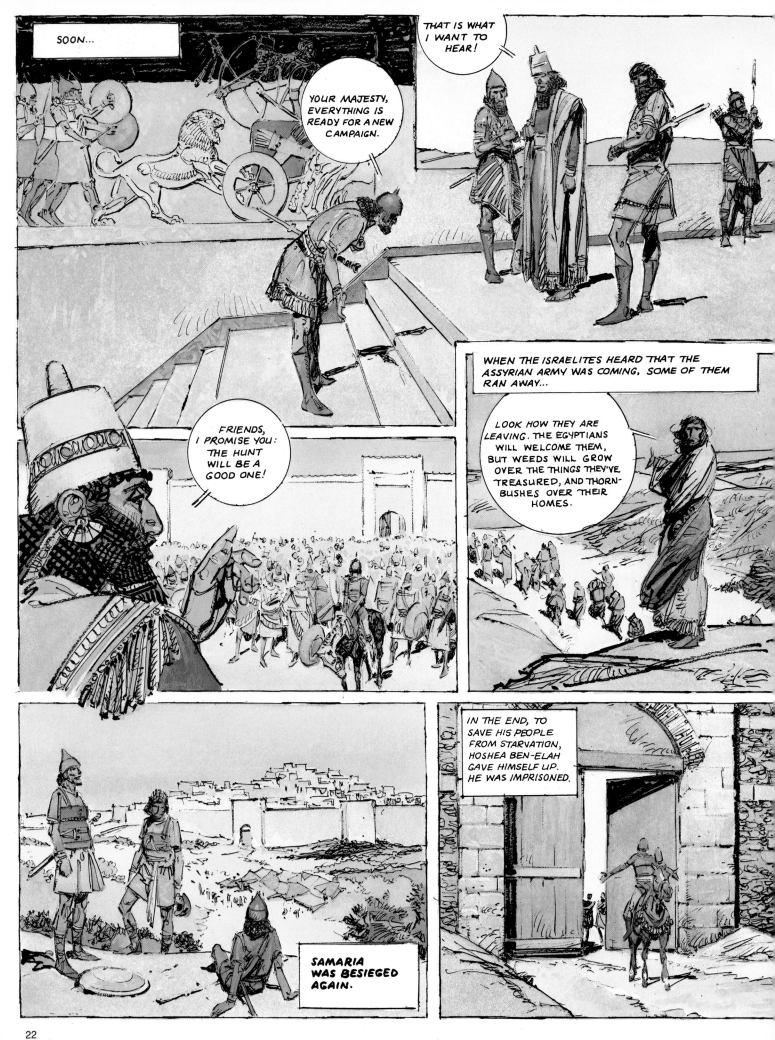

IN THE CENTRE OF THE CITY A GROUP OF MEN STILL FOUGHT AND HOPED. A FEW MONTHS LATER...

SHALMANE-SER IS DEAD! THIS IS OUR CHANCE!

LET'S CALL THE PEOPLE TO REVOLT.

DEATH TO THE ASSYRIANS!

BENEATH THE CITY WALLS THE MEN OF SAMARIA ATTACKED THE ASSYRIANS...

BUT THE ASSYRIAN ARMY RETURNED IN FORCE UNDER **SARGON II**, THE NEW KING, WHO DECIDED TO FINISH THINGS OFF.

SHOW NO MERCY!

AFTER THREE YEARS OF SIEGE, FAMINE, AND BATTLES, SARGON II TOOK SAMARIA. THE ISRAELITES HAD WAITED IN VAIN FOR HELP FROM EGYPT. MOST OF THE SURVIVORS WERE DEPORTED TO ASSYRIA*

* 722/721 BC.

23

THE PROPHET ISAIAH

SCENARIO : Etienne DAHLER
DRAWING : José BIELSA

AFTER SAMARIA WAS CAPTURED BY THE ASSYRIANS IN 722/721 BC, THE KINGDOM OF ISRAEL CEASED TO EXIST, BUT THE KINGDOM OF JUDAH WAS STILL THERE, LOYAL TO THE ASSYRIANS.

MY NAME IS ISAIAH, WHICH MEANS 'THE LORD IS SALVATION,' AND THIS IS JERUSALEM, MY CITY...

I WAS BORN HERE, GREW UP HERE, AND HERE I AM TODAY, THE LORD'S PROPHET.

BUT, LET'S SIT IN THE SHADE, AND I'LL TELL YOU THE WHOLE STORY.

ONE DAY I REMEMBER IT AS IF IT WERE YESTERDAY... IT WAS THE YEAR THAT KING UZZIAH DIED...*

I WAS IN THE TEMPLE, WHEN SUDDENLY I SAW THE LORD, SITTING ON A THRONE, VERY HIGH. THE SERAPHS WERE AROUND HIM, CALLING TO ONE ANOTHER:

HOLY, HOLY, HOLY! THE LORD IS ALMIGHTY!

40 BC. The king's other name was Amaziah.

FOUNDATIONS OF THE TEMPLE BEGAN TO SHAKE, THE TEMPLE ITSELF WAS FILLED WITH SMOKE... N I SAID:

THERE IS NO HOPE FOR ME! I'M LOST, BECAUSE EVERY WORD I SPEAK IS SINFUL... AND WITH MY OWN EYES I'VE SEEN THE LORD!

THEN ONE OF THE SERAPHS FLEW DOWN TO ME, CARRYING A BURNING COAL HE HAD TAKEN FROM THE ALTAR WITH A PAIR OF TONGS, AND HE SAID TO ME: LOOK, THIS HAS TOUCHED YOUR LIPS; NOW YOUR GUILT IS GONE!

THEN I HEARD THE VOICE OF THE LORD. HE SAID: WHOM SHALL I SEND? WHO WILL BE MY MESSENGER? AND I REPLIED, HERE I AM; SEND ME!

THAT SAME YEAR MY WIFE GAVE BIRTH TO A BOY.

HIS NAME WILL BE SHE'AR JASHUB* BECAUSE AFTER GREAT SORROW A REMNANT OF ISRAEL WILL COME BACK.

* A remnant - a few - will come back.

SOON AFTERWARDS, STRONG IN THE TASK I HAD RECEIVED FROM GOD, I SET OUT FOR SAMARIA...

DOOM ON THOSE WHO CALL EVIL GOOD AND GOOD EVIL, WHO TURN DARKNESS INTO LIGHT AND LIGHT INTO DARKNESS!

THEIR ROOTS WILL ROT; THEIR FLOWERS WILL BLOW AWAY LIKE DUST, BECAUSE THEY HAVE REJECTED THE LAW OF THE LORD.

AMOS AND HOSEA BEFORE HIM, ...H CONDEMNED THE CORRUPTION OF ISRAEL ...ANNOUNCED THE JUDGEMENT OF GOD.

MAN OF GOD, STAY WITH US.

NO! THESE PEOPLE DON'T WANT TO LISTEN. I'M GOING!

AND THAT IS HOW I CAME BACK TO JERUSALEM AFTER SOME YEARS AWAY.

MOTHER! COME QUICKLY! FATHER HAS COME BACK!

...E KINGDOM OF JUDAH WAS DOING WELL. ...T ISAIAH NOTICED MANY INJUSTICES, ...D HE INTERRUPTED A HAPPY ...EAST...

...IS MY ...N TO SING YOU ...METHING!

MY FRIEND HAD A LOVELY VINEYARD... HE WORKED ON IT, PLANTED THE BEST VINES, AND WAITED FOR FINE GRAPES...

...BUT THE ONLY GRAPES WERE SOUR! HE WAS FURIOUS! SO HE BROKE DOWN THE WALL AROUND IT, AND LEFT THE BRAMBLES TO GROW OVER IT!

OH!

YES, YOU SHOULD LAMENT, BECAUSE THE WINE-FARMER IS GOD, AND YOU ARE THE VINEYARD!

32

WHEN THEY LEARNED THAT ISRAEL AND ARAM WERE MARCHING AGAINST JUDAH, AHAZ AND HIS PEOPLE WERE IN A PANIC.

THE COURT MOVED TO TOPHETH.

AND THERE KING AHAZ...

MOLOCH, I SACRIFICE MY SON TO YOU SO THAT JERUSALEM WILL BE SAVED!

ON THE WAY BACK THE KING MET ISAIAH AND HIS SON...

AHAZ, DON'T BE AFRAID! THEY WANT TO DESTROY YOU, BUT IT WON'T HAPPEN. THIS IS THE WORD OF THE LORD.

IN SPITE OF ISAIAH'S WORDS OF HOPE, KING AHAZ STILL SENT MESSENGERS TO THE ASSYRIAN KING.

SO YOU DON'T TRUST GOD? VERY WELL! ASK FOR A SIGN!

NO, I WON'T PUT THE LORD TO THE TEST!

WELL, THEN, THE LORD HIMSELF WILL GIVE YOU A SIGN. A YOUNG GIRL WILL BECOME PREGNANT...

...AND GIVE BIRTH TO A SON, AND SHE'LL CALL HIM IMMANUEL *

34

* God is with us.

BUT BEFORE THE BOY IS OLD ENOUGH TO CHOOSE BETWEEN GOOD AND EVIL, THIS LAND WILL HAVE BEEN DESTROYED.

WHAT DOES ISAIAH MEAN?

YOUR MAJESTY, I THINK I UNDERSTAND...

ISN'T THERE A YOUNG GIRL, ABIJAH, WHO HAS JUST JOINED YOUR HAREM? SHE'LL GIVE YOU A NEW HEIR...

...WHO'LL REIGN OVER JUDAH, BUT ONLY AFTER A TIME OF GREAT HARDSHIP.

YOU MAY BE RIGHT. BUT IT SEEMED TO ME ISAIAH MEANT MORE THAN THAT.

MY FRIENDS, NOBODY WANTS TO LISTEN TO ME! THEY TRUST IN ASSYRIA OR EGYPT MORE THAN IN THE LORD! BUT THAT DOUBLE-DEALING WILL COST US DEAR!

35

THE ARMIES OF DAMASCUS AND SAMARIA WERE ALREADY LAYING SIEGE TO JERUSALEM. THE CITY WAS FULL OF REFUGEES.

LOOK OVER THERE! OUR VILLAGE IS ON FIRE!

THEY'LL STEAL EVERYTHING, THAT IS FOR SURE!

BUT SOON...

THEY'RE LEAVING! THEY'RE LEAVING!

THEY'VE HAD TO LIFT THE SIEGE! ASSYRIA MUST HAVE ANSWERED OUR CALL!

THE ALLIES WENT HOME, BUT DESTROYED EVERYTHING ALONG THE WAY.

YOUR COUNTRY IS DESTROYED; YOUR TOWNS ARE BURNED TO THE GROUND. FOREIGNERS RANSACK YOUR FIELDS; THEY BECOME A DESERT BEFORE YOUR VERY EYES!

SOME TIME LATER ISAIAH RECEIVED GREAT ENCOURAGEMENT...

THE LORD HAS PROMISED ME ANOTHER CHILD... AND THIS IS HIS NAME...

MAHER-SHALAL-CHASH-BAZ?*

YES, BECAUSE BEFORE HE KNOWS HOW TO SAY 'MOTHER' AND 'FATHER' THEY'LL TAKE ALL THE WEALTH OF THE KINGDOM OF ARAM AND OF THE KINGDOM OF ISRAEL TO THE ASSYRIAN KING!

* Quick loot, fast plunder.

36

SEVERAL YEARS LATER, WHILE THE ASSYRIAN KING, SARGON II, WAS BUILDING A MAGNIFICENT PALACE AT KHORSABAD...

...A NEW ALLIANCE WAS BEING FORMED AGAINST HIM...IN JERUSALEM KING HEZEKIAH WAS WORRIED...

YOU SAY THE PHILISTINES? WITH THE EDOMITES AND THE MOABITES?

YOUR MAJESTY! COME AND SEE!

IT IS ISAIAH!

WHAT HAS HAPPENED TO HIM? HE IS NAKED!

IT IS HIS WAY OF TELLING US WHAT IS GOING TO HAPPEN TO THE ALLIANCE AGAINST THE ASSYRIANS

WILL WE BE DEPORTED?

WE'LL TRUST ISAIAH, AND NOT MAKE ANY MOVE.

THAT WAS A WISE DECISION, BECAUSE IN 711 THE ALLIES WERE WIPED OUT BY SARGON'S REGIMENTS!

AFTER MANY VICTORIOUS CAMPAIGNS, SARGON II DIED IN 705. THEN THE PHILISTINE PRINCES WENT TO SEE HEZEKIAH.

THIS IS THE RIGHT TIME FOR US TO REBEL.

ISAIAH, WHAT DO YOU THINK?

THE PHILISTINES SHOULD NOT BE GLAD, EVEN THOUGH THE ROD THAT BEAT THEM IS BROKEN... WHEN ONE SNAKE DIES, A WORSE ONE COMES IN ITS PLACE. A SNAKE'S EGG HATCHES INTO A FLYING DRAGON!

WELL, ISAIAH, HOW SHALL WE REPLY TO THESE PRINCES?

THAT THE LORD HAS FOUNDED ZION, AND HIS SUFFERING PEOPLE WILL FIND SAFETY THERE.

A LITTLE WHILE LATER HEZEKIAH CALLED A DOCTOR...

WELL?

YOUR MAJESTY, NOTHING CAN BE DONE; YOU HAVE LEPROSY.

TELL THE KING I'M HERE.

ISAIAH ARRIVED ON THE SCENE...

DON'T BE TOO HAPPY TO SEE ME, HEZEKIAH! I'VE COME TO TELL YOU THAT YOU'RE GOING TO DIE!

43

LORD! LORD! REMEMBER ME!

GUARD, COME WITH ME!

LORD, TAKE PITY ON YOUR SERVANT!

THEN GOD'S WORD CAME TO ISAIAH...

GO AND TELL HEZEKIAH: I HAVE HEARD YOUR PRAYER; I WILL ADD 15 YEARS TO YOUR LIFE.

BRING A PASTE OF FIGS; PUT IT ON THE ULCER, AND THE KING WILL BE CURED.

SARGON DIED, AND HIS SON SENNACHERIB SUCCEEDED HIM. THE ENEMIES OF ASSYRIA PREPARED A NEW ALLIANCE. BABYLON GOT IN TOUCH WITH JERUSALEM, BUT HEZEKIAH TURNED TO EGYPT...

YOU'RE TAKING GIFTS TO A NATION THAT WILL GIVE YOU NO HELP OR SUPPORT.

THREE DAYS LATER HEZEKIAH WENT UP TO THE TEMPLE TO THANK GOD.

JERUSALEM WAS SAVED, BUT THE KINGDOM OF JUDAH WAS PLUNDERED BY THE SOLDIERS AS THEY FLED.

A BRANCH WILL COME FROM THE TREE OF JESSE, AN OFFSPRING BORN OF HIS ROOTS. THE SPIRIT OF THE LORD WILL REST ON HIM...

THEN THE WOLF WILL LIVE IN PEACE WITH THE SHEEP; THE LEOPARD WILL SLEEP ALONGSIDE THE GOAT; THE CALF, LION CUBS, AND CATTLE WILL FEED TOGETHER, AND A LITTLE CHILD WILL HERD THEM.

ABOUT TEN YEARS LATER...

ISAIAH, THE 15 YEARS YOU WON FOR ME ARE NEARLY OVER...

HEZEKIAH, YOU CAN SLEEP HAPPILY: JERUSALEM IS STILL STANDING!

MY TASK IS FINISHED TOO, HEZEKIAH.

LET THIS BE A WITNESS FOR THE FUTURE: 'THIS NATION REFUSES TO LISTEN TO THE PROPHETS... IT IS LIKE A HIGH WALL WITH A CRACK RUNNING DOWN IT...'

'... SUDDENLY IT WILL COLLAPSE!'

JERUSALEM CELEBRATED, THANKING GOD FOR PUTTING THE ASSYRIANS TO FLIGHT.

WITHIN YOUR TEMPLE, O GOD, WE MEDITATE ON YOUR UNFAILING LOVE. MOUNT ZION REJOICES, THE VILLAGES OF JUDAH ARE GLAD BECAUSE OF YOUR JUDGEMENTS.

Psalm 48